FAMOUS BIBLE P[

PROPHETS

WITH FOLD·OUT PAGES

Written by Daryl Lucas
Illustrated by Robert C. Durham

Tyndale House Publishers, Inc.
Wheaton, Illinois

NOAH

Noah and his family packed up everything they owned. They put everything on a big ship. Then they packed food for a long journey. Finally, they gathered a male and a female of every animal. They put the animals on the ship, too.

Other people laughed at the sight. "Look at that! A ship in the middle of dry land!" they said. "Where will it sail?"

Noah tried to explain. "God will flood the earth because none of you will listen to him."

"Nonsense," people said. "Nobody believes in God. You are a foolish man!"

Noah tried to ignore them. But it was hard. Only his family believed him. Noah felt lonely.

Noah and his family got on the ship. God shut the door. Inside, they waited. Outside, people were still laughing and making fun of Noah. Would it ever rain as God said?

A week later, it began to sprinkle. Then it rained and rained and rained. For ten days, twenty days, thirty days it rained. Soon a mighty flood came. The water swept everyone away. Only Noah, his family, and the animals were safe.

After forty days the rain stopped. The floodwaters dried up. The ship rested on dry land. And everyone on the ship got out. "Thank you, God!" they said.

ELIJAH

"Elijah is stupid," said one person in the crowd. "He says Baal isn't a real god. He says he knows the only real God. But nobody believes in Elijah's God but him."

"Well, you saw what happened," said another. "The prophets of Baal prayed all day. They danced and yelled and cut themselves. 'Send fire, Baal!' they said. But nothing happened. Maybe Elijah is right."

"I don't know who to believe in," someone else said.

The crowd watched as Elijah made a table of stones. He put wood and meat on the table.

Then he dug a ditch around it. Finally, Elijah poured water over the wood. There was so much water that it filled the ditch.

The crowd waited quietly. Surely the wood was too wet to burn now! What would happen? Baal didn't send fire. Would God?

Elijah prayed aloud, "O Lord, show them that you are God."

Suddenly fire came down from the sky! It burned up the meat on the table of stones. It burned up the wet wood. It boiled away the water in the ditch. It burned up everything and then it stopped. Smoke rose from the stones and ashes.

The stones were covered with black soot.

Everyone shook with fear. "The Lord is God! The Lord is God!" they said. Then everyone knew that Elijah was right. His God *was* the real God.

ISAIAH

Isaiah wanted to serve God. He wanted that more than anything else in the world. One day, Isaiah looked up and saw a huge throne. A bright light shone in his eyes and filled the room.

Isaiah felt shivers from his head to his toes. He was terribly afraid!

Angels sang loudly. "God is holy! Everybody knows how great God is!" Suddenly there was smoke everywhere.

Isaiah trembled. "I am doomed!" he said. "I have done bad things. I have said bad things. I am not good enough to be God's servant."

Isaiah saw fire nearby. Hot coals glowed in the fire. Just then an angel picked up a hot coal. The angel came toward Isaiah. His knees knocked together with fear. What was the angel going to do to him?

"God loves you," said the angel. "When this coal touches your lips you will know that God has forgiven you. Then you can be his servant."

The coal touched Isaiah's lips. But it didn't burn! Instead,

Isaiah felt better inside. God really had forgiven him.

Then God said, "I need a prophet."

Isaiah replied, "I will go. Send me!" And God did.

DANIEL

King Darius looked worried. "Are you scared?" he asked his friend Daniel.

"No sir," said Daniel. "God will protect me in the lions' den. He knows I am innocent."

The king's men laughed at him. They hated Daniel. "*Nobody* survives the lions' den," they said. "Maybe a young man could fight the lions. But you are eighty years old. The lions will tear you apart!"

The king didn't want Daniel to die. But Daniel had broken a law. The law said no one should pray to God.

Daniel loved God. He prayed to him every day. Now Daniel had to be thrown to the hungry lions.

"Heh, heh, heh," the king's men laughed. They pushed Daniel into the den. Would the king ever see Daniel again?

The next morning, King Darius ran to the den. He called out to Daniel through the gate. "I couldn't sleep all night, Daniel," he said. "Are you all right? Did your God save you?"

"He did, Your Majesty!" said Daniel. "God shut the lions' mouths!"

The king smiled. He ordered his men to open the gate. They let Daniel out. God had saved his servant Daniel.

JONAH

The sailors were scared. They didn't want to throw Jonah overboard. But Jonah said the storm was his fault. "I disobeyed God," he said. "Now God is angry with me. If you throw me overboard, the storm will stop."

The sailors knew Jonah was right. They had no choice. They threw Jonah into the water.

Splash! Jonah moved his arms and kicked his legs. Where would he go? He was in the

middle of the sea. The storm and wind had stopped. But Jonah could not swim forever.

He began to get tired. The waves were too strong. He grew weaker and weaker.

Jonah began to sink. "O God, help me!" Jonah prayed.

Just then, a giant fish swallowed Jonah. Inside the fish, Jonah could not see, but he could breathe. He was so happy that he prayed. "Thank you, God!" "I thought I was going to drown. I said, 'Help me, God!' And

you rescued me! Thank you so much!"

For three days Jonah rode in the fish's belly. Finally, it spit him out onto a beach. Jonah did what God wanted from that day forward.

JOHN THE BAPTIST

John the Baptist lived in the desert. He ate grasshoppers and wild honey. Day after day he told the people the same thing. "The Savior is coming soon. Stop doing bad things and start doing good!"

Many people came out to hear John. Some did what he said. Others did not. But everybody wondered who John was. "Maybe he's Elijah," some said. "Elijah didn't die. He could have come back."

"Or, maybe he *is* the Savior,"

said some others.

"You are all wrong," said John. "I'm not the Savior. But I know the Savior is coming. He is greater than I. I am not even good enough to untie his shoes."

"Wow," the people said. John was a great man. If he wasn't the Savior, who was? And when would the Savior come?

Then one day, John pointed. "Look!" he said to the crowd. "There he is!" Everyone looked. It was Jesus, from Nazareth. "That man is the Savior," said John. "He will take away the sins of the whole world. He is the one I talked about. I know for sure that he is the Son of God."

Everyone was amazed. Many people followed Jesus after that day.

Read more about these
PROPHETS
in the Bible

NOAH

In the Old Testament

Genesis 6:11 — 7:11

ELIJAH

In the Old Testament

1 Kings 18:30-38

ISAIAH

In the Old Testament

Isaiah 6:1-8

DANIEL

In the Old Testament

Daniel 6:16-22

JONAH

In the Old Testament

Jonah 1:9-2:10

JOHN THE BAPTIST

In the New Testament

John 1:19-34